Music to My Ears

by Leila C. Edwards
illustrated by Diane Greenseid

Harcourt
SCHOOL PUBLISHERS

Printed in China

ISBN 10: 0-15-350665-2
ISBN 13: 978-0-15-350665-9

Ordering Options
ISBN 10: 0-15-350600-8 (Grade 3 On-Level Collection)
ISBN 13: 978-0-15-350600-0 (Grade 3 On-Level Collection)
ISBN 10: 0-15-357852-1 (package of 5)
ISBN 13: 978-0-15-357852-6 (package of 5)

1 2 3 4 5 6 7 8 9 10 985 12 11 10 09 08 07 06

I have loved music for as long as I can remember. Mama says I was singing before I was talking. She says that I sang in my crib, and I wasn't just making noises, but really singing. I sang whatever I heard on the radio or TV, and I still do.

My brother, Anthony, says I am a "music-head." I guess he's right, but the music is not just in my head. Music is in all of me, all of the time.

Almost any kind of music makes me want to move, and my body goes whatever way feels right. I have even squirmed in my seat before when music was playing. Once at a school assembly, I sang and rocked in my seat without knowing it. I suddenly noticed all the other kids looking at me, and I turned red.

I have wondered why other people don't feel music as strongly. Anthony likes music. He has plenty of CDs, and sometimes I catch him dancing around while he listens. He does not dance or sing when there is no music, however, and I do that all the time. Even at dinner, sometimes I sing. I don't realize I'm doing it, but I guess there is just music playing inside me all the time.

I thought that I was the only person who felt this way until I met Mrs. Lewis who lives in our building. Mom and I were coming home from the store. Mrs. Lewis had several bags, and she dropped her wallet as she went through the door.

"Quick, Celia, please pick that up and take it to her," said Mom. I picked up the wallet and ran ahead, but Mrs. Lewis was already gone.

Anthony and I took the wallet to Mrs. Lewis, and Mrs. Lewis and I became friends.

One day, she said, "Celia, you are always singing when I see you."

"I guess I can't help it," I replied.

She laughed and said, "I was the same way and, in fact, I think I am still the same way. Do you like to dance?"

"I don't really know how to dance, but I love the feeling," I answered.

"Well, that's dancing," she said.

One day, Mrs. Lewis invited us into her apartment. There were designs hanging on the walls, and there were statues on tables. There were paintings in bright colors, and there were lots of pictures.

While she and Mama were talking, I walked over to the piano because I wanted a closer look at all the pictures. Mrs. Lewis was in most of them, and in most of them, she was dancing!

In some of the pictures, she was with a lot of dancers. In some of the pictures, she was by herself. There were pictures of Mrs. Lewis as a young girl, and there were pictures of her as an adult. There were also pictures of her as she looked now. Some pictures showed her standing with other people. Some of these photos were autographed. In one picture, she was in front of a group of children in dance clothes.

I turned around, and Mrs. Lewis was smiling at me. "There are a lot of years on that piano, aren't there, Celia? My career has been a patchwork of things. I've had a lot of jobs, all so that I could keep dancing. I could never sit still."

I nodded again because I knew that feeling.

"I went many places and met many people. They were all people like me who felt the feeling."

"Do you still dance, Mrs. Lewis?" I wanted to know.

"Yes, I do, because I cannot *not* dance, Celia. It's just a part of me, but mostly, now, I teach," Mrs. Lewis replied.

"What kind of dance do you teach, Mrs. Lewis?" Mama asked.

"Why, I teach all styles including tap, jazz, ballet, modern— just about anything. Swing is back in now, just as it was when I was a girl, but I suppose I like ballet most of all."

"In ballet, you learn to feel your body very well. You learn exactly where you are. You learn balance. Balance is the key to all dance, Celia. Of course, I didn't know that when I started. I thought dance was just about moving."

"It's not?" I asked.

"Dance is movement in balance," she said. "I'll bet your body already knows part of it. We get in time with the music, and then we move from one place to another place with the music."

"Yes," I said, nodding. I could feel that as I imagined myself dancing.

"Well, balance is important in all three places."

"Three places?" I asked.

"The position you start from is one," Mrs. Lewis said. "The position you move to is the second. The position you take as you move from one to another is a third, even in the simplest move. You must be in balance all three times."

Finally, Mama laughed and said. "It's time for Mrs. Lewis to dismiss this class, but I want to speak with Mrs. Lewis for a moment."

Anthony and I went on ahead, and Mama stayed and talked to Mrs. Lewis for a minute. When Mama came home, she gave me the best news ever.

I am going to learn ballet, and I am going to learn how well I can balance because tomorrow is my first day in Mrs. Lewis's dance school!

Think Critically

1. Why does Anthony call Celia a "music-head"?

2. Why was it lucky that Mrs. Lewis lost her wallet?

3. Why does Mrs. Lewis say that "there are a lot of years on that piano"?

4. How does Celia feel about what Mrs. Lewis says about balance?

5. In what way has Celia changed at the very end of the story?

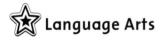 **Language Arts**

Write a Paragraph Celia feels that music is special to her. What is something that interests you so deeply that you feel it is a part of you? Write a paragraph describing this interest.

School-Home Connection There are many kinds of dance. Ask friends and family the names of some dances they know. Try to learn some of the dances.